Clubbing

Michael Alcott

Published in association with
The Basic Skills Agency

Hodder & Stoughton

A MEMBER OF THE HODDER HEADLINE GROUP

Acknowledgements
Cover: Fred Van Deelan
Illustrations: Mike Bell

Orders: please contact Bookpoint Ltd, 39 Milton Park, Abingdon, Oxon OX14 4TD. Telephone: (44) 01235 400414, Fax: (44) 01235 400454. Lines are open from 9.00–6.00, Monday to Saturday, with a 24 hour message answering service. Email address: orders@bookpoint.co.uk

British Library Cataloguing in Publication Data
A catalogue record for this title is available from The British Library

ISBN 0 340 74907 5

First published 1999
Impression number 10 9 8 7 6 5 4 3 2 1
Year 2004 2003 2002 2001 2000 1999

Typeset by Fakenham Photosetting Ltd, Fakenham, Norfolk.
Printed in Great Britain for Hodder & Stoughton Educational, a division of Hodder Headline Plc, 338 Euston Road, London NW1 3BH by Athenaeum Press, Gateshead, Tyne & Wear.

About the play

The People

- **Ben**
- **Emma**

The Time

Evening

The Scene

A nightclub.

***Ben** goes to a table where a young woman is sitting.*

*He speaks to **Emma**.*

Act 1

Ben Would you like to dance?

Emma No thanks.

Ben Go on.

Emma I said no thanks.

Ben Just one dance.

Emma I said no. N–O. No.
In big, big letters. Am I clear?

Ben No.

Emma No?

Ben Yes.

Emma I don't want to dance with you.

Ben Oh! You should have said.
What's your name?

Emma Emma.

Ben Emma.

Emma Yes, Emma.
Do you have to repeat everything?

Ben Do I have to repeat everything?
No. No.
I don't have to repeat everything.
I'm Ben. B–E–N. Ben.
As you didn't ask.

Emma Maybe I didn't want to know your name.

Ben Well you didn't say you did.
And you didn't say you didn't.
So now you know. Ben.
And you are Emma.
May I sit down? Emma, please.

Emma It's a free world.

Ben It's a free world, is it?
Am I free to dance with you?
I'm not free to dance with you,
am I?
So it isn't a free world, Emma.
Nice name, Emma.

Emma It's a rotten name.

Ben It's a lovely name. Emma. Soft.
Sexy.

Emma It's not your name, is it!

Ben (*laughs*) No it isn't.
It's a girl's name.
See me as Emma! Hello, darling.

Emma (*laughs*) Don't be so stupid.

Ben Stupid! Who's being stupid.
May I sit here?

Emma As I said . . .

Ben It's a free world. Yes, yes.

(*Ben sits at the table*)

Ben Now we know each other.

Emma Know each other! You're joking!

Ben Well . . . I've seen you round college. All term.

Emma No! You amaze me.

Ben I'm serious.

Emma I *am* a student there. So you might see me from time to time.

Ben What are you studying?

Emma Hair.

Ben Hair!

Emma Hair. That's what I said.
You do have to repeat everything,
don't you?

Ben You want to be a hairdresser?

Emma A real brain box!

Ben You're studying hairdressing.
That explains it.

Emma Explains what?

Ben Your hair.

Emma My hair?

Ben It's wonderful. A shaft of gold,
falling down your shoulders …

Emma It's not natural.

Ben It looks good to me.

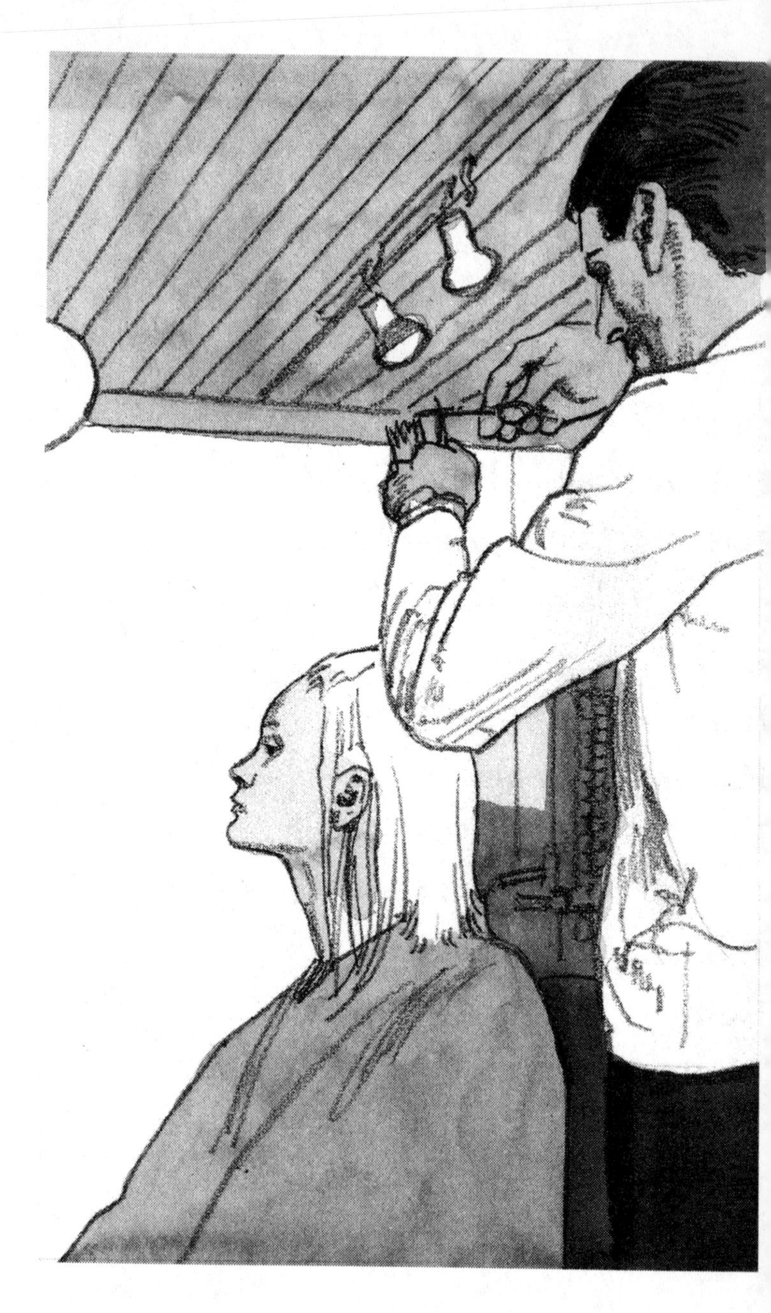

Emma Your hair could do with some work on it.

Ben Nothing wrong with my hair.

Emma Apart from the colour …
the style … the length …
apart from those small things it's wonderful.

Ben I think *you're* wonderful.
I've been watching you all term.
A dance with you would make my night. But I knew you'd say no.
It's the way I walk, I suppose.

Emma I don't want to dance. Full stop.

Ben Can I tell you a secret?

Emma Then it won't be a secret.

Ben Ah! Well. At the moment it is my secret. Between me and me.
If I tell you it will still be a secret.
Between me and you.

Emma Very clever!

Ben Here it is. I dream about you.

Emma Do you!

Ben Wonderful, sexy dreams …
I hold you in my arms. There!
But even so you won't dance with me because of my funny walk.

Emma I didn't say that.

Ben But it's true. It's true, isn't it?

Emma You're embarrassing me.

Ben Sorry, Emma. I don't want to embarrass you.
But at least I tell the truth.

Emma Well … not that it matters …
but … you do walk a bit funny.

Ben There you are! I knew it.
You've said it. Feel better now?

Emma What do you mean by that?

Ben Facing the truth.
We often feel better when we face
the truth. I know that.
All my life I've had to face the truth.

Emma What?

Ben That I walk funny.
That people laugh at me.
I know they do. I hear them when
I walk down the corridor.
It used to upset me. Not now.
I just feel sorry for them.
The truth is … I can only walk the
way I walk. It's me.
But … as you say, it's a free world.
If people want to laugh at me I
suppose they can.

Emma Did you have an accident?

Ben Not in the way you mean.

Emma In what way then?

Ben Do you know what cerebral palsy is, Emma?

Emma Cerebral what?

Ben Cerebral palsy.

Emma Never heard of it.

Ben It's what I have.
Which is why I walk the way I walk. When I was born ...
my brain ... my mum tells me ...
my brain was damaged ...
as simple as that ...
and I have to live with it.

Emma That's rotten.

Ben (*laughs*) Like living with a name like Emma!

Emma Don't be stupid.
It's a lot worse than that.

Ben But I can still dance.
If somebody will dance with me.

Emma What are you studying?

Ben To be a chef.

My Dad has a small restaurant.

Italian. I might work with him.

Emma Are you Italian?

Ben Half. My Mum's Irish.

My Dad's Italian.

I'm a sort of Irish stew.

Emma (*laughs*) My Mum's Irish.

Never knew my Dad. He took off.

Ben What about a drink?

Would you like a drink?

Emma Okay. Thanks.

Ben And what will it be?

Champagne … whisky …

gin and tonic … water?

Emma Water. Sparkling.

With ice and lemon.

Ben Big drinker!

Act 2

*(**Ben** goes to the bar on the other side of the dance floor to buy the drinks. When he comes back **Emma** is not there. She is dancing with someone else. **Ben** sits at the table. **Emma** returns to the table.)*

Emma Oh! I didn't think you were coming back. Thanks for the drink anyway.

Ben You're a great dancer.

Emma It's easy with him.
He's my boyfriend.

Ben Kevin Jones?

Emma Or was. You know him?

Ben He's in my maths set at college.

Emma He was very upset to see you at this table.

Ben It's a free world … remember?

Emma Too right. He's jealous.

Ben Of me?

Emma Yes. Of you. I think I'll wind him up good and proper.

Ben But why?

Emma Just to annoy him.
Come and sit close to me.
Put your arm round me.

Ben Hold on. I don't want to get into this.

Emma Into what?

Ben You and Kevin.

Emma Have you ever had a girlfriend?

Ben Well . . .

Emma Tell the truth. You were on about the truth just now.

Ben Sort of . . .

Emma Which means you haven't.
So come on. You said I'm the girl of your dreams. Now's your chance. Put your arm round me . . . kiss me on the cheek.

Ben I don't think so, Emma.

Emma Go and dance with somebody else then.

Ben I will.

Emma If anybody will dance with you.

Ben That's not fair.

Emma Some of us can dance with anybody we choose.
Others just can't.
I'm one of those people who can dance with anybody …

Ben Enjoy your drink, Emma.
I'm going to dance … with somebody else.

(***Ben** dances with another girl.*
*Then he returns to **Emma's** table*)

Emma Well, well.
What a good mover you are.

Ben In spite of my funny walk.

Emma You said it.

Ben I see Kevin is dancing a lot.

Emma To annoy me.
Come and put your arm round me.

Ben Emma. I told you.
You're being stupid.

Emma Then dance with me.

Ben Dance with you!

Emma Yes. Dance with me.
Your dream girl.
Now's your chance.

Ben Emma.

Emma Yes?

Ben When I came to the club tonight,
all I wanted to do was talk to you
and dance with you.
But now something's changed.

Emma I've given you a chance.

Ben You've given me a chance to annoy
your boyfriend.

Emma So?

Ben That's not what I want.
When I dance with someone it's
because I want to dance with
them. Not to hurt someone else.

Emma So what do you want?

Ben You say you can dance with anybody in this club.

Emma Yes. I can.

Ben You can't.

Emma What does that mean?

Ben I can tell you right now. There is at least one person here that you can't dance with.

Emma Who's that?

Ben (*laughs*) I'll leave you to work that one out.

I Never Done Nothing

My Mistress' Eyes

Craig

The Phone Box

Not Just a Game

The Trip

The Head's Office

A Great Day Out!

Beach Babe

Spooky!

Mine Shaft

Sleeping Rough

Mobile Phoney